Easter
ACTIVITY BOOK
and
BIBLE STUDY

**Ages
8-12**

HSM

About the Title of this Book

The word "Easter" does not appear in the Bible. There are different theories regarding where this word originates, and some prefer not to use the word Easter when referring to the day we celebrate Christ's resurrection. Whether you call it Easter, Resurrection Day, or another term, we hope this activity book and Bible study helps you learn more about what Jesus has done for you.

Easter Activity Book and Bible Study (Ages 8-12)

ISBN: 978-1-7359547-6-9

Copyright © 2023 by Hide and Seek Ministries

Published by Hide and Seek Ministries

Springfield, MO 65801

www.hideandseekministries.com

This Book
Belongs to:

_____

How to Use This Book

This book is divided into **11** sections. Each section has **6** pages to complete.

PAGE 1

First, read the Bible verses in your Bible. Then answer the questions about what you read.

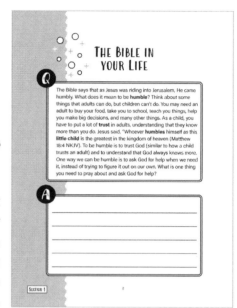

PAGE 2

On the next page, answer the question about applying what you read to your own life.

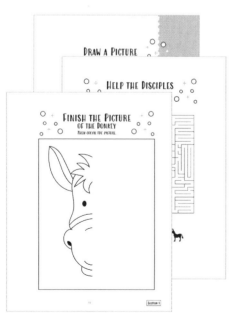

PAGES 3–5

Complete the fun activities on the next 3 pages.

PAGE 6

Read the "Things to Note" page, and then you're done with that section!

Section List

Here is a list of the sections you will be completing in this book.
The answers to the activities start on page 75.

Section	Event	Scripture	Page
1	Jesus rides into Jerusalem on a donkey	Matthew 21:1–11 Zechariah 9:9	7
2	Judas agrees to betray Jesus and Jesus celebrates Passover	Matthew 26:14–30 Luke 22:7–13	13
3	Jesus predicts that Peter will deny Him	John 13:36–38 Matthew 26:31–35 Zechariah 13:7	19
4	Jesus says He is leaving but is sending a Helper	John 16:1–15	25
5	Jesus prays in the Garden of Gethsemane	Matthew 26:36–46 Luke 22:39–46	31
6	Jesus is arrested and faces the Sanhedrin	Matthew 26:47–68 Luke 22:63–65	37
7	Peter denies Jesus	Matthew 26:69–75 Luke 22:54–62	43
8	Judas dies and Jesus faces Pontius Pilate	Matthew 27:1–31	49
9	Jesus dies on a cross	Matthew 27:32–56 Psalm 22:16–18	55
10	A soldier pierces Jesus' side and Jesus is buried in Joseph's tomb	John 19:31–42 Matthew 27:62–66	61
11	Jesus rises from the dead	Matthew 28:1–15	67

READ

☐ Matthew 21:1–11

☐ Zechariah 9:9

1 What animal did Jesus ride on when He entered Jerusalem?

a. Horse

b. Donkey

c. Camel

2 What did people put on the road as Jesus passed by?

a. Mats and straw

b. Leaves and twigs

c. Clothes and tree branches

3 What did the people say as Jesus passed by?

a. Hosanna

b. Favored One

c. Great King

PROPHECY FULFILLED

Around **500 years** before Jesus rode into Jerusalem on a donkey, a prophet named Zechariah prophesied that there would be a humble King riding on a donkey's colt (Zechariah 9:9).

DID YOU KNOW?

In 2 Kings 9:13, people also placed their clothes on the ground when a man named Jehu became king. In those days, spreading clothes on the ground was a way that the people greeted a king.

THE BIBLE IN YOUR LIFE

Q

The Bible says that as Jesus was riding into Jerusalem, He came humbly. What does it mean to be **humble**? Think about some things that adults can do, but children can't do. You may need an adult to buy your food, take you to school, teach you things, help you make big decisions, and many other things. As a child, you have to put a lot of **trust** in adults, understanding that they know more than you do. Jesus said, "Whoever **humbles** himself as this **little child** is the greatest in the kingdom of heaven (Matthew 18:4 NKJV). To be humble is to trust God (similar to how a child trusts an adult) and to understand that God always knows more. One way we can be humble is to ask God for help when we need it, instead of trying to figure it out on our own. What is one thing you need to pray about and ask God for help?

A

DRAW A PICTURE
OF SOMETHING YOU ARE PRAYING ABOUT

Help the Disciples Find the Colt

Finish the Picture
of the Donkey
Then color the picture.

Things to Note

IN SECTION 1

 Jesus riding into Jerusalem on a donkey is called the "Triumphal Entry."

The word **triumph** means a great victory.

Many people thought Jesus was coming to save them from the Romans (who were ruling over them). But Jesus was planning to save them from sin by dying on the cross. Jesus' triumph was defeating death by rising from the dead three days later.

Jesus chose to ride on a donkey into Jerusalem one week before His death. A donkey was an animal that royalty rode because donkeys were a symbol of peace.

 One day, Jesus will come to earth a second time. When He does, He won't be riding a donkey; He will be riding a white horse, which is a symbol of victory in battle (Revelation 19:11).

END OF SECTION 1

12

30 **READ** ☐ Matthew 26:14–30
☐ Luke 22:7–13

1 What did Judas get for betraying Jesus?

a. 10 pieces of gold

b. 30 pieces of silver

c. 60 pieces of silver

2 What does the Bible say about Judas? (Also see John 12:4-6.)

a. He was an honest man.

b. He was a thief.

c. He was a good friend.

3 What does the bread represent?

a. Jesus' blood

b. Jesus' body

c. Jesus' heart

4 What does the cup represent?

a. Jesus' blood

b. Jesus' body

c. Jesus' heart

DID YOU KNOW?

At the end of the Passover meal, the Bible says Jesus and His disciples sang a hymn. The hymn they likely sang can be found in your Bible, in Psalms 113–118. These psalms are also known as "Hallel." Pay attention to the words in Psalm 116 and imagine Jesus singing them the night before He died.

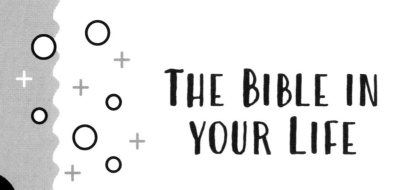

THE BIBLE IN YOUR LIFE

Q

Jesus ate the Passover meal with His disciples, just as God's people had done every year. The Passover meal was meant to help God's people remember what God had done for them (read more on page 18). The word "remember" appears in the Bible more than 200 times. David said, "I remember the days of old; I meditate on all you have done; I reflect on the work of your hands" (Psalm 143:5 CSB). Many times, the Bible says the Israelites forgot what God had done for them, and they turned away from God. Purposefully remembering what God has done for you is very important and will help your faith. Think of something that God has done for you and write about it below.

A

DRAW A PICTURE
OF SOMETHING GOD HAS DONE FOR YOU

DID YOU KNOW?

Jesus told His disciples that the bread represented His body and the cup represented His blood. This is called the Lord's Supper. Jesus also said His blood is the start of a new covenant. A covenant is a very special promise. Read more about this new covenant in Hebrews 8:6-13.

Can you find the coins?

Find the 4 coins that have the number 30 and color them.

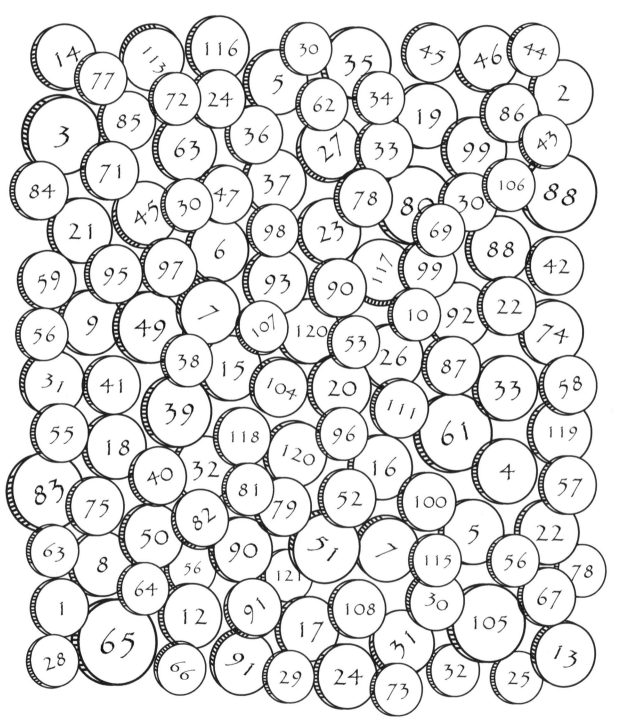

Write the letter of the alphabet that comes AFTER each letter.

Jesus said,

"For this is my _____ _____ _____ _____ _____ of the
       A   K   N   N   C

_____ _____ _____ _____ _____ _a_ _____ _____ ,
 B   N   U   D   M   M   S

which is _____ _____ _____ _____ _____ _____ out for
       O   N   T   Q   D   C

_____ _a_ _____ _____ for the forgiveness of
 L   M   X

_____ _____ _____ _____ ."
 R   H   M   R

Matthew 26:28 CSB

SECTION 2

Things to Note

IN SECTION 2

Do you remember when God sent Moses to save the Israelites from being slaves in Egypt? You can read about this story in the book of Exodus. When God sent Moses to Egypt, He also sent the 10 plagues. (Remember the frogs, flies, darkness, and other bad things?) When God sent the tenth and final plague, He told the Israelites to sacrifice a lamb and put its blood on their doorposts. Then, when God saw the blood, He would "pass over" their house and save them from the plague. **This was the very first Passover.** Every year after that, the Israelites ate the Passover meal to remember how God had saved them in Egypt. And this is the meal that Jesus and His disciples ate together.

The lamb's blood symbolized what Jesus would one day do. Just as the lamb's blood saved the Israelites in Egypt, Jesus' blood saves the whole world from sin. The Bible calls Jesus "our Passover Lamb" (1 Corinthians 5:7).

END OF SECTION 2

READ

- ☐ John 13:36–38
- ☐ Matthew 26:31–35
- ☐ Zechariah 13:7

1

Who did Jesus say would deny Him?

a. John

b. Matthew

c. Peter

2

How many times did Jesus say he would deny Him?

a. 1 time

b. 2 times

c. 3 times

3

Where did Jesus say He would go after He was raised from the dead? (Hint: Read Matthew 26:32.)

a. Galilee

b. Judea

c. Samaria

PROPHECY FULFILLED

Jesus quoted a prophecy that Zechariah gave around **500 years before**, saying the disciples were like sheep and would "scatter" away from their Shepherd (Jesus).

DID YOU KNOW?

In the Bible days, it was common for there to be many roosters in the towns and cities. The first crowing of roosters often happened around midnight and the second happened around dawn (when the sun started to rise). If someone makes the comment "before the rooster crows," it is usually understood as meaning before dawn.

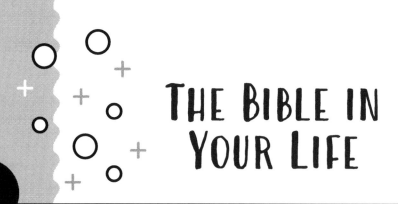

The Bible in Your Life

Q

Jesus said that Peter would deny Him three times. Peter argued with Jesus and said, "Even if everyone falls away because of you, I will never fall away" (Matthew 26:33 CSB). Peter argued with Jesus, but notice that Jesus did not argue with Peter. When the Lord has spoken, He has spoken. There is no need for Him to argue about it. In the Bible, God says, "I will not...change what my lips have said" (Psalm 89:34 CSB). Can you think of any promises that God has given you? It does not matter what things seem like in this world, God will never change what He has promised you. **Read the following promises in your Bible, choose one, and write the verse below.**

- Psalm 32:8   • Matthew 11:28   • Philippians 4:19

A

DRAW A PICTURE
OF SOMETHING GOD HAS PROMISED YOU

DID YOU KNOW?

The three Bible verses on the previous page are not the only promises in the Bible. There are many, many more! Here are a few more promises:

- Joshua 1:9
- Isaiah 40:29
- Malachi 3:10
- Mark 11:24
- John 3:16
- John 8:36
- Romans 8:28
- James 1:5
- James 4:7
- 1 John 1:9

Find the Hidden Word

Each word below is the name of a disciple. Unscramble each word and put a letter in each box next to the word. When you're finished, find the hidden word by writing the letters that appear in the darker boxes.

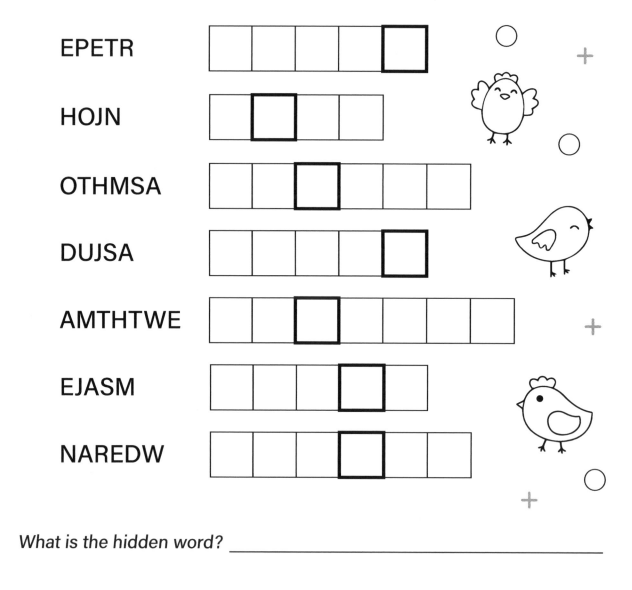

EPETR

HOJN

OTHMSA

DUJSA

AMTHTWE

EJASM

NAREDW

What is the hidden word? _____

Here is a list of the 12 disciples in case you need help.

Peter	Andrew	Matthew	Simon
James	Philip	Thomas	James
John	Judas	Thaddeus	Bartholomew

COLOR THE PICTURE OF THE ROOSTER

Things to Note

IN SECTION 3

♥ The news that Jesus was going to leave was very troubling to the disciples. And not only was He leaving, but Jesus said that Peter would deny Him three times. Peter thought that was impossible, and he didn't understand. Then Jesus said, "Do not let your hearts be troubled" (John 14:1). Jesus says the same to you today. How does Jesus calm your troubled heart? He gave six promises in John 13 and 14 that you should always remember.

1. By believing in Jesus, you are going to Heaven. This world is only temporary.

2. You don't have to wait for Heaven. You can have a relationship with God right now.

3. You can always talk to God through prayer.

4. You will always have the Holy Spirit to help you.

5. You are never unloved. You will always have the Father's love.

6. God has given you the gift of peace. Focus on Him and you will have peace no matter what you are facing.

END OF SECTION 3

READ

☐ John 16:1–15

1

Jesus said after He died, the disciples would be all alone.

a. True

b. False

2

Jesus said He would send the

_____ when He

goes away.

Hint: Read John 16:7.

3

Jesus said the Spirit of _____ was coming.

a. Fear

b. Truth

c. Obedience

4

Who is the the Spirit of Truth?

a. The Holy Spirit

b. Peter

c. Mary

DID YOU KNOW?

In John 16:7, Jesus said He would send the Holy Spirit after He dies. In this verse, the word Jesus used to describe the Holy Spirit is different depending on which version of the Bible you read. Your Bible may say Jesus would send the *Helper*, *Advocate*, *Comforter*, *Counselor*, *Friend*, or *Companion*. All of these words are good descriptions of the Holy Spirit.

THE BIBLE IN YOUR LIFE

Q

You may wish that you could see Jesus every day just as the disciples did. But Jesus said it was better that He leaves, so He could send the Holy Spirit. The Holy Spirit is God Himself, and you don't have to wait on Him like the disciples did. When you believe in Jesus, the Holy Spirit lives inside you (1 Corinthians 6:19)!

The Holy Spirit will do such things as comfort you, guide you, tell you what is yet to come, and lead you to the truth. **Have you made the choice to believe in Jesus? Does the Holy Spirit live inside you?** Write your answers below.

Then read what happened when the Holy Spirit did come to the disciples in Acts 2:1-13.

A

_____

_____

_____

DRAW A PICTURE
OF SOMETHING THAT SYMBOLIZES THE HOLY SPIRIT

Need help?
Read this.

DID YOU KNOW?

We can't see the Holy Spirit. However, the Bible describes the Holy Spirit as a dove, fire, wind, and water. Read the following verses to find out more:

Matthew 3:16
Acts 2:1-4
John 7:37-39

SECTION 4

HIDDEN PHRASE WORD SEARCH

```
C O M F O R T E R
O A D V O C A T E
U H F R I E N D O
N S E A L L O R D
S T E A C H E R L
E H E L P E R Y S
L P A U T H O R I
O R G U I D E I T
R R R E V E A L E R
```

ADVOCATE

AUTHOR

COMFORTER

COUNSELOR

FRIEND

GUIDE

HELPER

LORD

REVEALER

SEAL

TEACHER

Hint: There are no diagonal words.

Write the letters you didn't circle on the lines below. Write them in the order they appear (from left to right, as if you were reading a book).

___ ___ ___ ___

___ ___ ___ ___ ___ ___

SOLVE THE CODE

Solve the code to find the answer to the question.

A	B	C	D	E	F	G	H	I
1	2	3	4	5	6	7	8	9

J	K	L	M	N	O	P	Q	R
10	11	12	13	14	15	16	17	18

S	T	U	V	W	X	Y	Z
19	20	21	22	23	24	25	26

What is one thing the Holy Spirit will do?

___ ___ ___ ___ ___   ___ ___ ___
7   21   9   4   5   25   15   21

___ ___ ___ ___   ___ ___ ___
9   14   20   15   1   12   12

___ ___ ___ ___ ___
20   18   21   20   8

John 16:13 NKJV

Things to Note

IN SECTION 4

For about three years, the disciples had spent most of their time being with Jesus. He was their teacher and friend, and they loved Him. When Jesus told them He was leaving, they were filled with sadness. But Jesus said it was better that He leaves, so that He could send the Holy Spirit.

When Jesus came to earth, He was fully God, but He was also fully human (Phil. 2:6-7). With His human body, He could only be in one place at a time. However, the Holy Spirit (the Spirit of God) can be in all places at the same time. Jesus can now be with you at the exact same time that He is with people on the other side of the world.

✝ Before Jesus died on the cross, the Holy Spirit would come and go. But after Jesus was raised from the dead, the Holy Spirit is now with you all the time. He will never leave you (Ephesians 1:13-14) and is here to teach you, comfort you, and help you.

END OF SECTION 4

READ

☐ Matthew 26:36–46
☐ Luke 22:39–46

1 How did Jesus feel when He was in Gethsemane?

a. Happy

b. Sorrowful and troubled

c. Angry

2 Luke said Jesus' sweat was like _____.

a. water

b. honey

c. drops of blood

3 What did Jesus do in the Garden of Gethsemane?

a. Sleep

b. Pray

c. Eat

4 According to Matthew, how many times did Jesus find the disciples sleeping?

a. 1 time

b. 2 times

c. 3 times

DID YOU KNOW?

The word "Gethsemane" means oil press. The Garden of Gethsemane where Jesus prayed is still in Jerusalem today, and it is full of ancient olive trees. They made olive oil from the olives on the trees.

31

SECTION 5

THE BIBLE IN YOUR LIFE

Q

When Jesus was praying in the garden, He was overwhelmed with sorrow because He was about to bear the sins of the whole world in His body (1 Peter 2:24). It's hard to imagine what that must have been like. But even so, Jesus said, "Yet not as I will, but as you will" (Matt. 26:39). Jesus always did what God wanted Him to do. He followed **God's will** (John 6:38). **God has a will (or a plan) for your life too** (Eph. 2:10). *How can you find and follow that plan?* Here are some things that will help you: (1) Put God first in every part of your life. (2) Spend time getting to know God by praying and reading the Bible. (3) Pay attention to the right things and guard your heart. If you don't guard your heart, it will be hard to hear from God. **What is something you can do to guard your heart?** Write your answer below. (Use the next page to help you.)

A

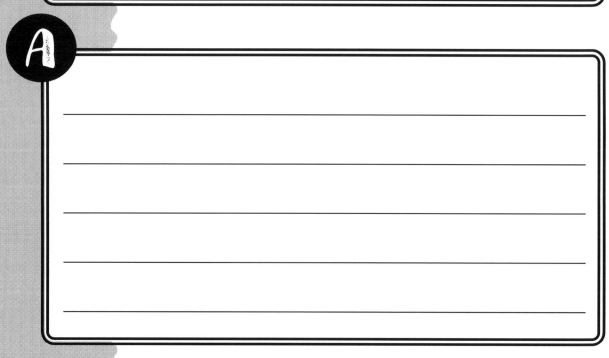

GUARD YOUR HEART

1 **Read**

Proverbs 4:23

Luke 6:45

Joshua 1:8

2 Because Adam and Eve chose not to listen to God, every person is born with sin. With sin, your heart is full of bad things, and you are separated from God.

Color the first heart a dark color to show that it is full of sin.

When you choose to believe in Jesus, and make Him your Lord and Savior, you are given a new and perfect spirit.

Then...

If you **choose** to guard your heart, you can get rid of the bad inside it.

How can you guard your heart?

Things enter your heart through your **eyes** and **ears**. To guard your heart, be careful what you look at and listen to.

Read your Bible every day and do what it says! God promises you will be blessed!

3 Leave the second heart white. This shows what happens to your heart when you guard it. White and clean!

33

Garden of Gethsemane Word search

```
P  W  C  M  Y  I  U  X  B  M
F  R  J  U  P  Q  S  D  E  Q
U  L  A  J  P  C  L  T  T  G
T  C  E  Y  Q  P  E  U  R  A
Z  S  L  S  E  J  E  X  A  R
E  T  W  C  H  R  P  O  Y  D
S  P  I  R  I  T  X  Y  E  E
V  C  M  M  H  T  Q  T  R  N
H  D  I  S  C  I  P  L  E  S
G  E  T  H  S  E  M  A  N  E
```

CUP	FLESH	PRAYER
BETRAYER	GARDEN	SLEEP
DISCIPLES	GETHSEMANE	SPIRIT

Hint: There are three diagonal words.

How Many Words Can You Make

out of the Word

GETHSEMANE

Things to Note

IN SECTION 5

When Jesus was praying in the garden, He said, "My soul is overwhelmed with sorrow to the point of death" (Matt. 26:38). He was troubled because He was about to "drink the cup" that His Father had prepared for Him. This means He was about to bear the sins of the whole world in His body (John 18:11, 1 Peter 2:24). The Bible says that God made Jesus "be sin for us" and become "a curse for us" (2 Cor. 5:21, Gal. 3:13). *Why did He do this?*

When Adam and Eve disobeyed God, sin entered the world. Now every person is born with sin, and sin separates you from God. (Imagine a big wall between you and God that no one can cross.) God says the punishment for the sin that is inside of you is death (Rom. 6:23). When Jesus suffered and died, He took that sin and the punishment away from you. When you believe in Jesus, it's like Jesus removes that big "wall," and you get to be with God forever.

END OF SECTION 5

READ

☐ Matthew 26:47–68

☐ Luke 22:63–65

1 What sign did Judas use to point out Jesus?

a. A hug

b. A kiss

c. A handshake

2 What name did Jesus call Judas? (*Hint: Read Matthew 26:50.*)

a. Betrayer

b. Friend

c. Brother

3 What did the disciples do when Jesus was arrested? (*Hint: Read Matthew 26:56*).

a. They fought the soldiers.

b. They ran away.

c. They were arrested too.

PROPHECY FULFILLED

Matthew tells us that Jesus was hurt badly. They spit on Him, beat Him, blindfolded Him, and mocked Him. Around **700 years** before, Isaiah prophesied that this would happen. You can read his prophecy in Isaiah 50:6.

DID YOU KNOW?

Matthew, Mark, Luke and John all write about a disciple cutting off the servant's ear. But only John tells us that it was Peter who did it (John 18:10). John is also the only one to tell us that the servant's name was Malchus. Luke is the only one to tell us what happened afterward: Jesus healed the servant's ear (Luke 22:51).

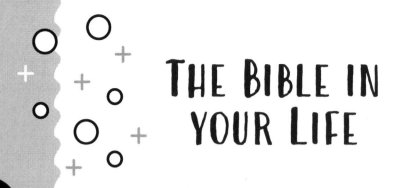

THE BIBLE IN YOUR LIFE

Q

When Jesus was brought to the high priest, the Bible says they were looking for something that Jesus did wrong. "They wanted to put him to death. But they did not find any proof" (Matt. 26:59 NIrV). Jesus was the only perfect person to ever live. He lived on earth for around 33 years and never once sinned. We are called to be like Jesus, but it is impossible for anyone to be perfect. Sometimes we make mistakes. The important thing is that when we do make a mistake, we recognize it and turn away from it.

The Bible says, "If we say that we have no sin, we deceive ourselves, and the truth is not in us. If we confess our sins, He is faithful and just to forgive us our sins and to cleanse us from all unrighteousness" (1 John 1:8-9 NKJV). When you ask God for forgiveness, it is like your sin is completely erased, as if it never happened. This doesn't mean we can sin all we want and ask for forgiveness later. Jesus said, "If you love me, obey my commands" (John 14:15 NIrV; also see 1 John 2:3-6 and Hebrews 10:26). Sin can affect your relationship with God. But we do know that He is always willing to forgive us.

Is there anything that comes to mind that you need to ask forgiveness for? You don't have to write your answer. You can say a silent prayer right now (or pray with someone you're with) and tell God about it.

DRAW A PICTURE
OF WHAT YOU THINK AN ARMY OF ANGELS WOULD LOOK LIKE

DID YOU KNOW?

Jesus said He could have called for more than 12 legions of angels to come save Him. One legion is equal to 6,000, so 12 legions are equal to 72,000 angels! And Jesus said He could call "more than" that.

The Bible also tells us about an army of angels in 2 Kings 6.

HELP PETER
FOLLOW JESUS

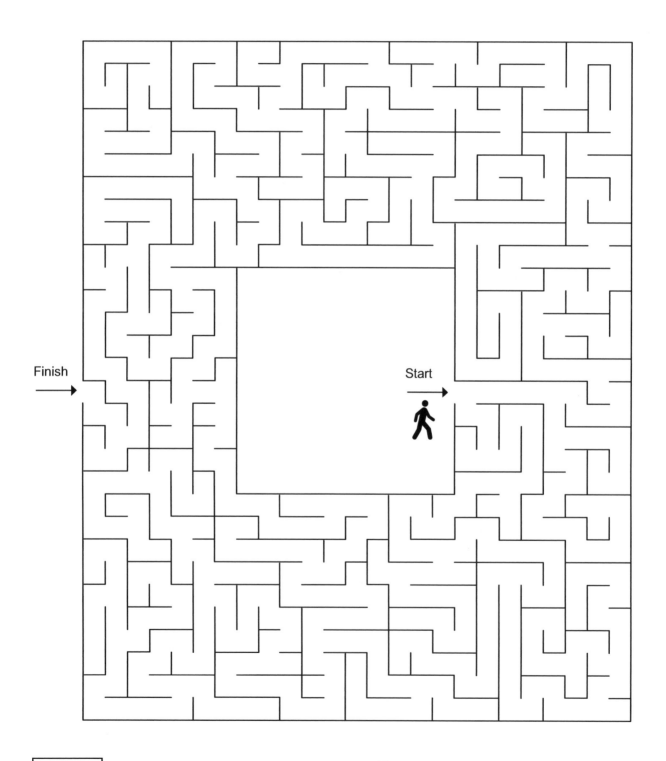

Finish

Start

CAN YOU FIND THE 8 DIFFERENCES?

Things to Note

IN SECTION 6

It was normal for disciples to kiss their teacher as a sign of honor and respect. But Judas used a kiss as a weapon. The Greek word that is used in Matthew 26:49 tells us that Judas kissed Jesus multiple times.

The fact that Judas came to Jesus with a great multitude of soldiers who had weapons shows that Judas didn't really understand Jesus. It seems that Judas thought they would have to search for Jesus and fight off the disciples in order to arrest Him. Instead, Jesus calmly surrendered. Judas didn't need to kiss Jesus as a sign. Jesus told the soldiers who He was.

You may have heard someone say, "If I could just see Jesus for myself, then I would believe in Him." Judas not only saw Jesus, but for nearly three years he saw Jesus perform miracles, heard His teachings, and he himself received power to cast out demons and heal diseases (Matthew 10:1). Yet Judas let greed get in the way, and he refused to see the truth.

END OF SECTION 6

READ

☐ Matthew 26:69–75

☐ Luke 22:54–62

1 After Jesus was arrested, Peter followed Jesus at a distance.

a. True

b. False

2 How many times did they question Peter about Jesus?

a. 1 time

b. 2 times

c. 3 times

3 Did Peter admit that he knew Jesus?

a. Yes

b. No

4 When Peter denied Jesus three times, the rooster crowed. What else happened?

a. Peter cried.

b. Jesus looked at Peter.

c. Both A and B.

DID YOU KNOW? In the book of John, we find out that the man who questioned Peter the third time was a relative of Malchus, the man who Peter wounded by cutting off his ear (John 18:26).

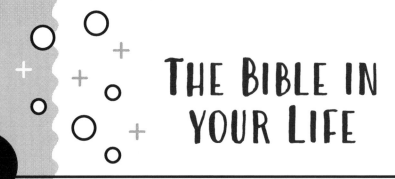

THE BIBLE IN YOUR LIFE

Q

Before Jesus was arrested, the Bible says the time had come for Jesus to tell His disciples that He would die and be raised from the dead. But the disciples didn't understand, and Peter argued with Jesus (Matthew 16:21-22). Jesus said Peter was "not thinking about God's concerns but human concerns" (Matthew 16:23 CSB). This is what Peter was also doing when he denied Jesus; he was not thinking about what Jesus had told him, but only what he could see happening at that moment. The Bible says that you should "set your mind on things above, not on earthly things" (Colossians 3:2). List some examples of what you think godly things and earthly things could be.

A

Godly Things   **Earthly Things**

_____   _____

_____   _____

_____   _____

_____   _____

_____   _____

Need help? See some examples on page 79.

DRAW A PICTURE
OF A GODLY THING
THAT YOU LISTED

DID YOU KNOW?

Another disciple was with Peter as he followed Jesus at a distance, but we are not told which disciple it was. The other disciple knew the high priest, and the disciple let Peter into the high priest's courtyard. That is where Peter denied Jesus (John 18:15-16).

FIND THE MESSAGE

Cross out all the letters that appear <u>exactly</u> 3 times. Write the remaining letters on the lines below, in the order that they appear (reading left to right, as you would read a book). When you're done, you should have crossed out 21 letters.

```
P  A  E  T  C  E  C  R  G  R
E  G  M  K  A  E  M  B  E  C
R  K  E  G  D  T  H  K  L  E
W  O  L  R  N  L  D  A  X  O
F  N  J  E  N  X  S  U  X  S
```

— — — — —

— — — — — — — — — —

— — — — — —

— — — — — —

Matthew 26:75 NKJV

Finish the Picture of the Rooster

Then color the picture

Things to Note

IN SECTION 7

Peter went through some hard times. He had watched Jesus (his teacher, friend, and Lord) get arrested and beaten as he followed Him at a distance. And then he denied Jesus three times, just as Jesus said he would. Peter never thought he would do such a thing. It was so devastating to him that he started weeping and ran off. What should Peter have done? What should you do if you also go through something hard?

If Peter would have focused on the words of Jesus, he would have remembered that Jesus had said to Peter, "Indeed, Satan has asked for you...But I have prayed for you, that your faith should not fail..." (Luke 22:31-32 NKJV). Peter should have listened to Jesus and trusted in His words, and that is what you should do too.

You have a Father in Heaven who loves you. Jesus has promised that He will never leave you, and He will always be there to help you, no matter what you're going through. Read and remember His words (the Bible), and trust in them.

END OF SECTION 7

 **READ** ☐ Matthew 27:1–31

1

When Jesus was sentenced to die, what did Judas do?

a. Fought the soldiers

b. Ran and hid

c. Returned the silver

2

Who had a bad dream about Jesus?

a. Peter

b. Pilate's wife

c. Barabbas

3

What did the soldiers put on Jesus?

a. A scarlet robe

b. A crown of thorns

c. A reed in His hand

d. All of the above

PROPHECY FULFILLED

A prophet named Isaiah said that even though Jesus would be treated badly and made to suffer, Jesus would not open His mouth (Isaiah 53:7). Around **700 years later**, Jesus kept silent when He was wrongly accused of sin, and Pilate marveled (Matthew 27:14).

DID YOU KNOW?

Out of all the people being held prisoner, Pilate chose the most well-known prisoner he had—Barabbas. Barabbas was a robber and a murderer (John 18:40; Mark 15:7). The crowd of people chose to release a robber and murderer into society instead of releasing Jesus.

THE BIBLE IN YOUR LIFE

Q

Jesus' closest friends (the disciples) had left Him alone. People were saying false things about Him, and crowds yelled to have Him crucified. The soldiers scourged, beat, and spit on Him. They put a crown of thorns on His head and made fun of Him. It may seem like Jesus was no longer in control. But in John 10:15-18, Jesus said, "I lay down my life for the sheep...No one takes it from me, but I lay it down on my own" (CSB). Jesus went through all the suffering because He wanted to and because His Father wanted Him to. He did it because **He loves you**. Copy this Bible verse on the lines below (John 3:16 NIV):

For God so loved the world that he gave his one and only Son...

A

DRAW A PICTURE
OF SOMETHING OR SOMEONE YOU LOVE

DID YOU KNOW?

The Jewish leaders didn't have authority to sentence anyone to death, but the Romans did. That's why they sent Jesus to be judged by the Roman governor named Pontius Pilate (John 18:31).

SOLVE THE PUZZLE

ACROSS

3. Crown of _____

5. Roman governor

DOWN

1. Returned 30 pieces of silver

2. Prisoner that was released

4. _____ of the Jews

FINISH THE MAZE

Start →

Finish

SECTION 8

Things to Note

IN SECTION 8

The Bible talks about a "first Adam" and a "last Adam." The first Adam was the first person in the history of the world. God made him from the dust of the ground, breathed into his nostrils, and put him on a perfect earth (Genesis 2:7).

The Bible says that Jesus is the last Adam (1 Cor. 15:45). Both the first Adam and the last Adam were tempted. The first Adam was tempted with fruit from a forbidden tree. He disobeyed God and death was brought into the world (sin, sadness, sickness, worry, fear, and so on). The last Adam (Jesus) was tempted for 40 days in the wilderness, and He obeyed God. The first Adam brought **death** into the world, but the last Adam brings **life** (Romans 5:18, 1 Cor. 15:22).

Jesus took our place and died for our sins so that we wouldn't have to. The Bible says, "For the wages of sin is death, but the gift of God is eternal **life in Christ Jesus** our Lord" (Romans 6:23). It also says that God "sent his one and only Son into the world that we might **live** through him" (1 John 4:9).

END OF SECTION 8

READ

☐ Matthew 27:32–56

☐ Psalm 22:16–18

1 Who carried the cross for Jesus?

a. Peter

b. Simon

c. Matthew

2 How many robbers were crucified with Jesus?

a. 2

b. 3

c. 4

3 What happened when Jesus died?

a. An earthquake

b. The veil in the temple was torn

c. People were raised from the dead

d. All of the above

4 PROPHECY FULFILLED

Around **1,000 years before Jesus** was crucified, David said that people would divide up Jesus' clothes and cast lots for them. And it happened just as David said it would (Psalm 22:18).

DID YOU KNOW?

Casting lots is mentioned over 70 times in the Bible. Although we are not sure exactly what type of lots were used, they were likely dice, sticks, or stones. And they were used to help make decisions. It is kind of like when someone flips a coin today.

THE BIBLE IN YOUR LIFE

Q

Some people think there is a list of things they must do to be able to go to Heaven. And they think if they make a mistake, they might not go to Heaven. They wonder if God truly loves them, or if God stopped loving them. If they get sick, they think, "I must have done something wrong, and God made me sick to punish me." They might even think, "I'm a pretty good person, so there's no way that God won't let me into Heaven." The last words Jesus said before He died were, "It is finished!" (John 19:30). *What was finished?* All that Jesus had come to do. You don't have to do something to earn your way to Heaven. Jesus did all the work for you. His work is finished, and it's a free gift. Make Jesus the Lord of your life and the gift is yours, even if you don't deserve it. Write this Bible verse on the lines below (Ephesians 2:8 NIrV):

Your salvation doesn't come from anything you do. It is God's gift.

A

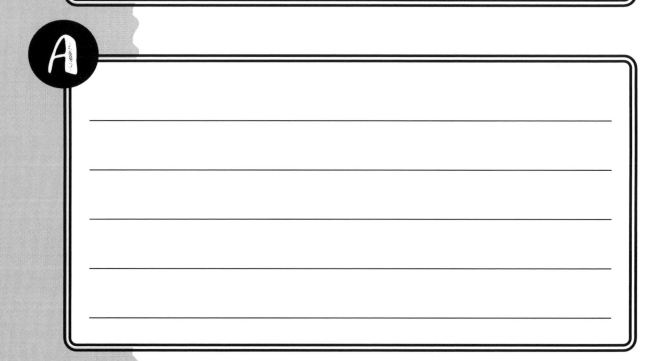

DRAW A PICTURE
OF A GIFT YOU HAVE RECEIVED

DID YOU KNOW?

Do you remember that Jesus is called the Passover Lamb (relating to what happened when God rescued His people in Egypt)?

When Jesus was on the cross, darkness covered the land for 3 hours before He died.

Before the very first Passover, there were 3 days of darkness in Egypt (Ex. 10:21-23).

SOLVE THE CODE

Solve the code to find the answer to the question.

A	B	C	D	E	F	G	H	I
26	25	24	23	22	21	20	19	18

J	K	L	M	N	O	P	Q	R
17	16	15	14	13	12	11	10	9

S	T	U	V	W	X	Y	Z
8	7	6	5	4	3	2	1

How does God show His love for us?

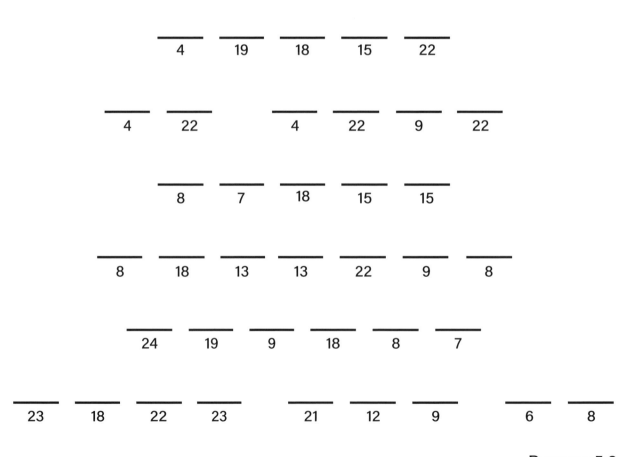

```
  __  __  __  __  __
   4  19  18  15  22

  __  __     __  __  __  __
   4  22      4  22   9  22

  __  __  __  __  __
   8   7  18  15  15

  __  __  __  __  __  __  __
   8  18  13  13  22   9   8

  __  __  __  __  __  __
  24  19   9  18   8   7

  __  __  __  __     __  __  __     __  __
  23  18  22  23     21  12   9      6   8
```

Romans 5:8

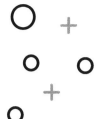

FINISH DRAWING
THE GIFT BOX

ADD DECORATIONS AND COLOR THE PICTURE

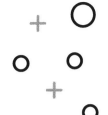

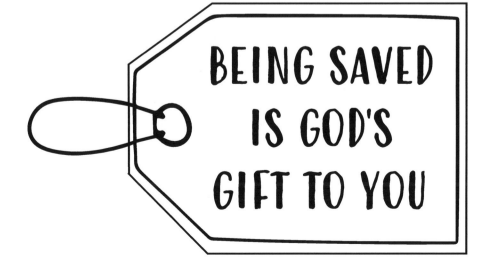

BEING SAVED
IS GOD'S
GIFT TO YOU

SECTION 9

Things to Note

IN SECTION 9

Before Jesus died, people had to sacrifice animals to be forgiven of sin. They had to do this over and over because an animal was not a perfect sacrifice, and it didn't completely take away sin. The sacrifices were meant to remind people of their sin. God was showing the people that they couldn't be perfect on their own, and they needed someone to save them (Hebrews 10:1-4).

There was a place inside the temple called the Holy of Holies (Hebrews 9:1-9). It was where God's presence was, and it was hidden behind a veil (or curtain). Only a high priest could go inside once a year to ask for forgiveness of sins for all the people. The veil symbolized a separation between God and people.

When Jesus died on the cross, that veil in the temple was torn in two. This meant there would be no more separation between God and His people. We no longer have to sacrifice animals or have a priest talk to God for us. Where animals were not perfect, Jesus was the perfect and final sacrifice. We now have the Holy Spirit and we can talk to God directly, any time we want to.

END OF SECTION 9

 **READ**

☐ John 19:31–42

☐ Matthew 27:62–66

1

What did the soldiers do to make sure Jesus had died?

a. Broke His bones

b. Stoned Him

c. Pierced His side

2

Who asked Pilate for the body of Jesus?

a. Joseph of Arimathea

b. Lazarus

c. John

3

Who brought myrrh and aloes to Jesus' body?

a. John

b. Nicodemus

c. Mary

PROPHECY FULFILLED

About **1,000 years** before Jesus was on earth, David wrote that Jesus' hands and feet would be pierced, His bones would not be broken, and evil people would stare at Him (Psalm 22:16-17).

DID YOU KNOW?

Joseph of Arimathea and Nicodemus were both members of the Jewish council (the group that put Jesus on trial and sent Him to Pilate). They were following Jesus in secret. If they had not been there when Jesus died, Jesus' body would have likely been carried off to a ditch without a proper burial.

THE BIBLE IN YOUR LIFE

It may be hard to think of Jesus as a human being. But the Bible says Jesus "became flesh and dwelt among us" (John 1:14 CSB). He was born with a mother, had a real human body, lived as being both fully human and fully God, and He died. Jesus experienced everyday life, just as we do. He was a child, grew up to be an adult, went through joy, sorrow, pain, hunger, tiredness, temptation, and more. The Bible says Jesus is able to understand what we go through, and He understands our weaknesses. He was "tempted in every way, just as we are" (Heb. 4:15).

Yet, Jesus is also God and has always existed. All things were created by Him and through Him (Col. 1:16). He has no beginning or end. Jesus lived a life as a human, but He also created you. He knows everything about you, and He understands and cares about what you're going through.

DRAW A PICTURE
OF JESUS' TOMB

DID YOU KNOW?

God told His people to celebrate Passover every year to remember what He had done for them in Egypt. When celebrating, God told them they should eat a lamb, but must not break any of its bones (Ex. 12:46). Jesus, who is called the Passover Lamb, also did not have any of His bones broken.

Unscramble the words. Some of them have been done for you.

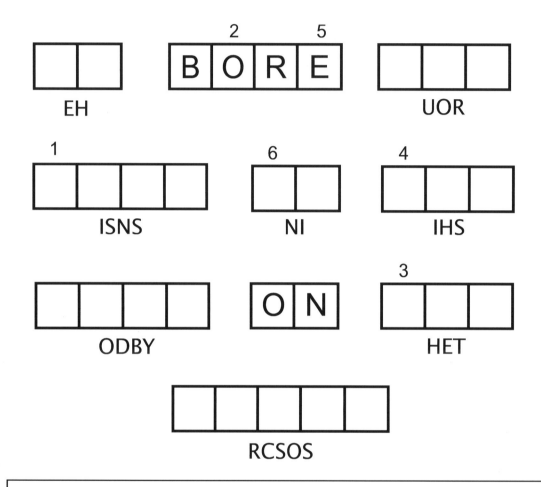

EH

2		5
B	O	R	E

UOR

ISNS

NI

IHS

ODBY

O N

HET

RCSOS

To finish the Bible verse, find the boxes that have numbers above them. Copy the letters from those boxes to the matching numbered boxes below.

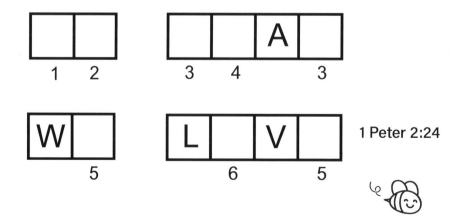

1 2

A
3 4 3

W
5

L V
6 5

1 Peter 2:24

Solve the Maze

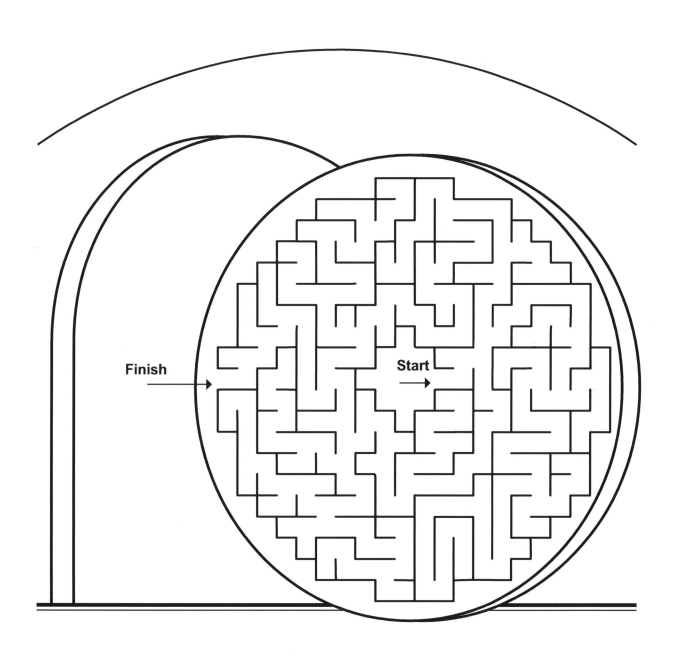

Things to Note

IN SECTION 10

A prophecy is a message from God about the future. A prophet is a person who gives the message. There are around 300 prophecies about Jesus that came true during His life, death, and resurrection.

Imagine you are living in the time of the Bible, and you keep hearing how a man is coming who will be called Lord, King, and the Son of God. You hear prophets say this man will be born in Bethlehem. He will heal people, perform miracles, and will teach parables. And although he will be called King, a friend will betray him. He will be sold for 30 pieces of silver. And he will be wounded, bruised, spit on, mocked, pierced, and killed with thieves at his side. Yet, while this happens none of his bones will be broken and his friends will scatter. Then after he dies, he will be buried in a rich man's tomb. If you were there to hear these things, would you believe them?

All these things were really said (or prophesied) about Jesus hundreds of years before He was born. Prophecy is more evidence that the Bible is truly the Word of God.

END OF SECTION 10

 **READ** ☐ Matthew 28:1–15

1 What did the guards do when they saw the angel?

a. Fought the angel

b. Ran away

c. Shook with fear

2 What did the angel tell the women?

a. Come back later.

b. He is risen.

c. You're at the wrong tomb.

3 Who met the women as they went to tell the disciples?

a. Jesus

b. Peter

c. Nicodemus

4 The elders told the guards at the tomb to lie about what happened.

a. True

b. False

DID YOU KNOW? The angel did not roll away the stone to help Jesus escape the tomb. The angel said, "Come and see the place where he lay" (Matthew 28:6). The angel rolled the stone away so others could *see* that Jesus had been raised from the dead.

THE BIBLE IN YOUR LIFE

You might be able to defeat your cousin in a game of checkers. One person can defeat another in a race, and one team can defeat another in a basketball game. But can any person say they can defeat death? Jesus can because He did. Jesus' death on the cross was not the only thing that saves us from sin, but the fact that He *defeated death*. He conquered it.

The Bible helps us see how important Jesus' resurrection is by explaining what it would be like if Jesus had not been raised from the dead. It says, "And if Christ has not been raised [from the dead], what we preach doesn't mean anything. Your faith doesn't mean anything either... Your sins have not been forgiven" (1 Corinthians 15:14, 17 NIrV). But Jesus was raised from the dead. He defeated it!

Jesus is not the only one that will be raised. The Bible says, "Christ is the first of those who rise from the dead. When he comes back, those who belong to him will be raised" (1 Corinthians 15:23 NIrV).

Now, read 1 Thessalonians 4:13-18 in your Bible.

DRAW A PICTURE
OF WHAT YOU THINK THE ANGEL AT THE TOMB MAY HAVE LOOKED LIKE

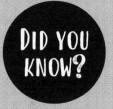

DID YOU KNOW?

Every year on "Good Friday" Christians remember that Jesus died on the cross. Then on Easter Sunday they celebrate that He rose from the dead.

SOLVE THE PUZZLE

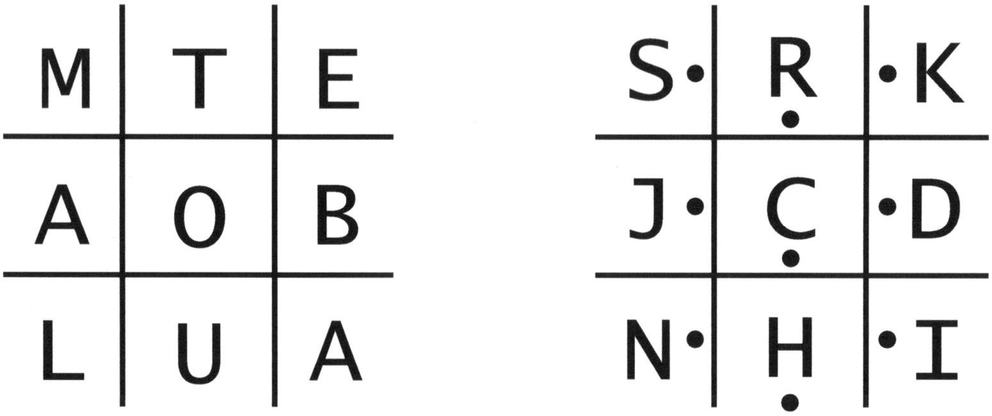

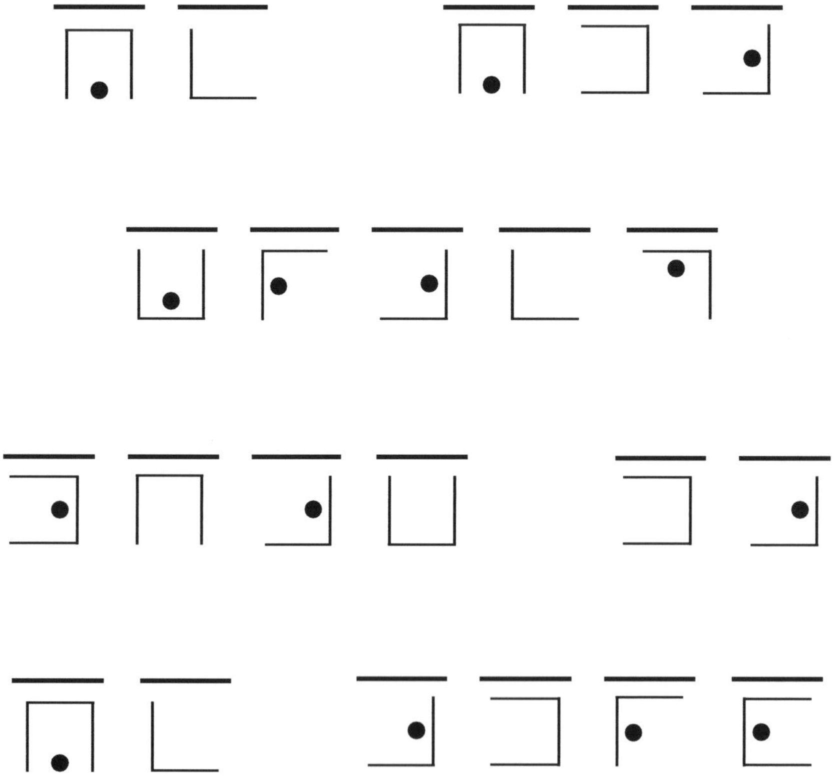

M | T | E
A | O | B
L | U | A

S· | R· | ·K
J· | Ç | ·D
N· | H· | ·I

Matthew 28:6

COLOR THE PICTURE

Things to Note

IN SECTION 11

When the women hurried away from the tomb to go tell the other disciples what they had seen and heard, the Bible says they were filled with joy. While they were on their way, suddenly Jesus was there with them.

Jesus had spent time teaching His disciples that He would die and be raised from the dead, but none of the disciples understood. The women had went to the tomb that morning thinking that Jesus was dead. How must they have felt when they saw Him alive and perfectly well?

What did they do when they saw Him? The Bible says they fell to His feet and worshiped Him.

If you believe in Jesus, you will one day go to a huge, perfect city that has a crystal clear river which flows from the throne of God. There will be the tree of life, and its leaves will bring healing. All the things in this city will be good; nothing bad. You will get to see Jesus face to face in a place called Heaven (Revelation 22:1-5). What do you think *you* will do when you see Him?

END OF SECTION 11

You've finished the book! Great job!

Billy

Find More Books and Activities at

www.hideandseekministries.com

Bobby

Just for Fun

One more question

How many bees can you find

in this book? _____

Find the answer on page 82.

Have you made Jesus your Lord and Savior?

The Bible says, " For God so loved the world that he gave his one and only Son, that whoever believes in him shall not perish but have eternal life" (John 3:16). It also says, " If you declare with your mouth, "Jesus is Lord," and believe in your heart that God raised him from the dead, you will be saved" (Romans 10:9). Do you believe in Jesus? Have you asked Him to forgive your sins and come into your life as your Lord and Savior?

_____

When you do, you are a child of God. All your sins are forgiven and wiped away as if they never happened. Read John 1:12 in the Bible and write the verse below.

_____

_____

_____

_____

ANSWERS

Page 7

1. b. Donkey

2. c. Clothes and tree branches

3. a. Hosanna

Page 10

Page 16

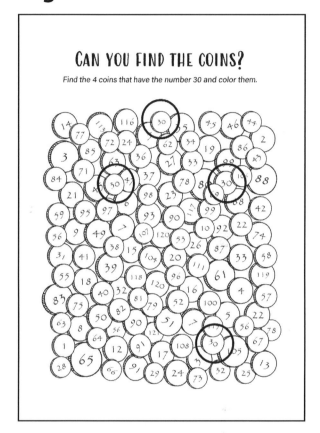

Page 13

1. b. 30 pieces of silver

2. b. He was a thief.

3. b. Jesus' body

4. a. Jesus' blood

ANSWERS

Page 17

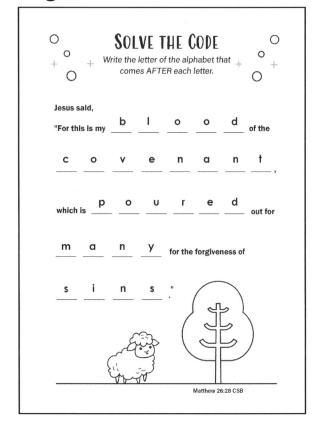

SOLVE THE CODE

Write the letter of the alphabet that comes AFTER each letter.

Jesus said,

"For this is my b l o o d of the

c o v e n a n t ,

which is p o u r e d out for

m a n y for the forgiveness of

s i n s ."

Matthew 26:28 CSB

Page 22

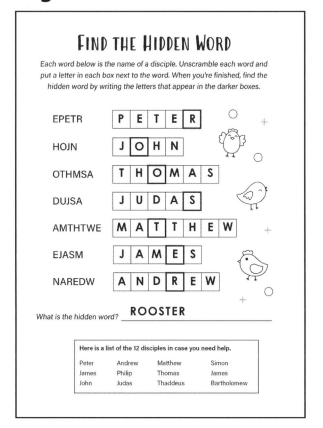

FIND THE HIDDEN WORD

Each word below is the name of a disciple. Unscramble each word and put a letter in each box next to the word. When you're finished, find the hidden word by writing the letters that appear in the darker boxes.

EPETR	P E T E R
HOJN	J O H N
OTHMSA	T H O M A S
DUJSA	J U D A S
AMTHTWE	M A T T H E W
EJASM	J A M E S
NAREDW	A N D R E W

What is the hidden word? **ROOSTER**

Here is a list of the 12 disciples in case you need help.

Peter	Andrew	Matthew	Simon
James	Philip	Thomas	James
John	Judas	Thaddeus	Bartholomew

Page 19

1. c. Peter

2. c. 3 times

3. a. Galilee

Page 25

1. b. False

2. Answers will vary depending on the Bible version. Answers could include Helper, Advocate, Comforter, Counselor, Friend, or Companion.

3. b. Truth

4. a. The Holy Spirit

ANSWERS

Page 28

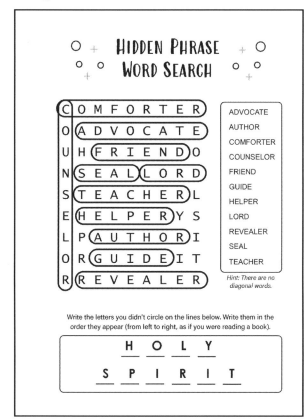

HIDDEN PHRASE WORD SEARCH

C	O	M	F	O	R	T	E	R
O	A	D	V	O	C	A	T	E
U	H	F	R	I	E	N	D	O
N	S	E	A	L	L	O	R	D
S	T	E	A	C	H	E	R	L
E	H	E	L	P	E	R	Y	S
L	P	A	U	T	H	O	R	I
O	R	G	U	I	D	E	I	T
R	R	E	V	E	A	L	E	R

ADVOCATE
AUTHOR
COMFORTER
COUNSELOR
FRIEND
GUIDE
HELPER
LORD
REVEALER
SEAL
TEACHER

Hint: There are no diagonal words.

Write the letters you didn't circle on the lines below. Write them in the order they appear (from left to right, as if you were reading a book).

H O L Y
S P I R I T

Page 29

SOLVE THE CODE

Solve the code to find the answer to the question.

A	B	C	D	E	F	G	H	I
1	2	3	4	5	6	7	8	9

J	K	L	M	N	O	P	Q	R
10	11	12	13	14	15	16	17	18

S	T	U	V	W	X	Y	Z	
19	20	21	22	23	24	25	26	

What is one thing the Holy Spirit will do?

G U I D E   Y O U
7 21 9 4 5   25 15 21

I N T O   A L L
9 14 20 15   1 12 12

T R U T H
20 18 21 20 8

John 16:13 NKJV

Page 31

1. b. Sorrowful and troubled

2. c. drops of blood

3. b. Pray

4. c. 3 times

ANSWERS

Page 34

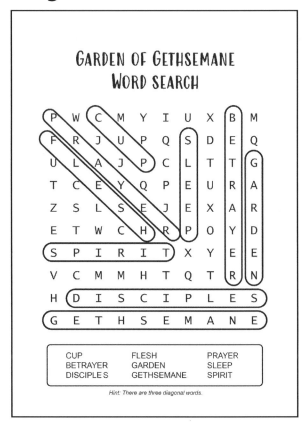

Page 40

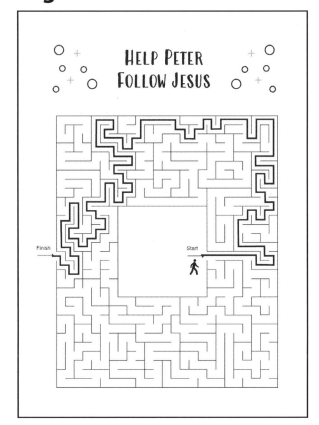

Page 35

Some example words include:

eat, game, gate, get, heat, man, mane, me, mean, meat, meet, neat, same, seam, see, seem, shame, she, sheet, team, the, them

Page 37

1. b. A kiss

2. b. Friend

3. b. They ran away.

ANSWERS

Page 41

Page 43

1. a. True

2. c. 3 times

3. b. No

4. c. Both A and B.

Page 44

Some possible answers might include:

Godly Things: God, Jesus, Holy Spirit, the Bible, prayer, church, church activities, family, friends, loving and helping others, Christian books and podcasts, Christian movies and music, godly hobbies, telling others about Jesus, God's plans for you

Earthly Things: money, material possessions (things you own or want to own), entertainment (TV, movies, video games, etc.), social media, fads

Page 46

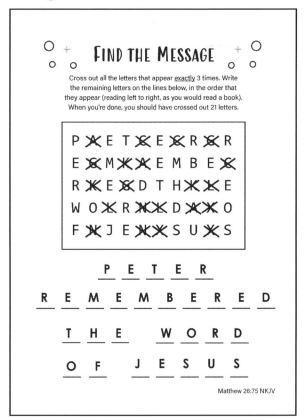

ANSWERS

Page 49

1. c. Returned the silver

2. b. Pilate's wife

3. d. All of the above.

Page 52

SOLVE THE PUZZLE

ACROSS

3. Crown of _____

5. Roman governor

DOWN

1. Returned 30 pieces of silver

2. Prisoner that was released

4. _____ of the Jews

Crossword answers:
- JUDAS
- BARABBAS
- THORNS
- KING
- PILATE

Page 53

FINISH THE MAZE

Start

Finish

Page 55

1. b. Simon

2. a. 2

3. d. All of the above

ANSWERS

Page 58

SOLVE THE CODE

Solve the code to find the answer to the question.

A	B	C	D	E	F	G	H	I
26	25	24	23	22	21	20	19	18
J	K	L	M	N	O	P	Q	R
17	16	15	14	13	12	11	10	9
S	T	U	V	W	X	Y	Z	
8	7	6	5	4	3	2	1	

How does God show His love for us?

W H I L E
4 19 18 15 22

W E   W E R E
4 22   4 22 9 22

S T I L L
8 7 18 15 15

S I N N E R S
8 18 13 13 22 9 8

C H R I S T
24 19 9 18 8 7

D I E D   F O R   U S
23 18 22 23   21 12 9   6 8

Romans 5:8

Page 64

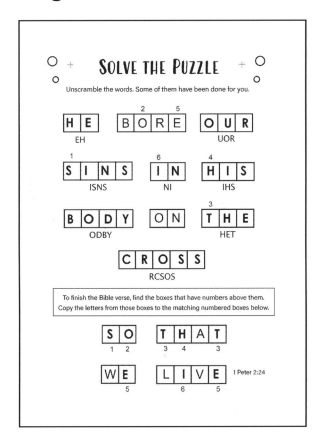

SOLVE THE PUZZLE

Unscramble the words. Some of them have been done for you.

H E   B O R E   O U R
EH   2   5   UOR

S I N S   I N   H I S
1   6   4
ISNS   NI   IHS

B O D Y   O N   T H E
ODBY   3
                    HET

C R O S S
RCSOS

To finish the Bible verse, find the boxes that have numbers above them. Copy the letters from those boxes to the matching numbered boxes below.

S O   T H A T
1 2   3 4 3

W E   L I V E   1 Peter 2:24
5   6   5

Page 61

1. c. Pierced His side

2. a. Joseph of Arimathea

3. b. Nicodemus

Answers

Page 65

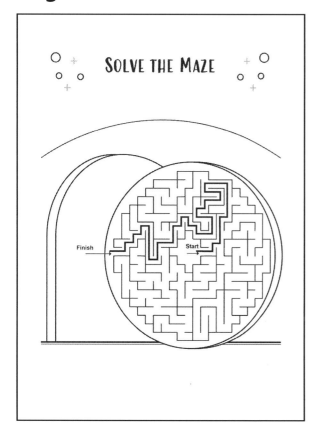

Page 70

Page 67

1. c. Shook with fear

2. b. He is risen.

3. a. Jesus

4. a. True

Page 73

There are 17 bees in this book!

Made in the USA
Middletown, DE
05 May 2023

30078640R00046